The
LONELIEST
GRIEF

The LONELIEST GRIEF

by
Karen Holford

*Statistics indicate that at least one in
every ten babies is lost through miscarriage.
Many mothers hide the sorrow inside
themselves and never talk about it because
they have found that most people do not
understand their feelings.
Here Karen shares her own experience of
miscarriage, provides practical guidance,
looks at the latest research and
demonstrates how to cope with the
emotional and spiritual issues surrounding
miscarriage.*

AUTUMN

HOUSE

Copyright © 1994 Karen Holford

Cover illustration: Carol Daniel

First published 1994

ISBN 1-873796 27 7

Published by
Autumn House Publications
Alma Park, Grantham, NG31 9SL, England

Preface

This is a book for women who have experienced the trauma of losing a baby through miscarriage. It is also for her friends and family, health professionals, chaplains and pastors. This is one mother's story. Each mother's story is different, and it is OK for a mother not to feel the same way as Karen, and not to find help and comfort from the same things as she did. The aim of the book is to help women work through their various emotions and find positive help and comfort in the middle of a bewildering and negative experience. It can also provide some spiritual answers to the questions some bereaved mothers ask God.

Acknowledgements

Thanks first of all to Bernie, my husband, who has always been a great stabilizing influence in my life, and without whose computer skills and hours of babysitting this book could not have been written. Thanks too, to my parents, for their continuous support in my life, and the strong spiritual background they gave me which has helped me through the ups and downs of life. Thanks to Heather Hanna RGN/RSCN for reading the script, and offering lots of helpful information on the medical side, as well as encouragement and practical advice. I also need to mention Shari Chamberlain and Pamela Mills, two good friends who helped me through the initial stages of grief in America, and did so much to encourage me.

And finally, thank You God, for always being there, and taking everything I've thrown at You and turning it into something beautiful. I hope and pray that this book will bring people closer to Your love at a time when they can feel so isolated and confused.

Contents

Foreword

IT HAS been estimated that as many as 1 in 10 pregnancies are unsuccessful and end in the very early stages of development. This very common event, therefore, is a part of the emotional rough and tumble of life to which many couples will be subjected. The very fact that it is such a common occurrence does nothing to diminish the impact on a couple of a lost pregnancy.

This is frequently kept as a very private and quiet event. There is not always, on the part of others, a full appreciation and respect for the powerful feelings of loss and bereavement that are usually engendered. If the process of grieving is not facilitated and experienced in a normal way, with the painful healing process being allowed to happen, then the psychological and emotional health of the mother and father can often be impaired for many months and years to come.

In this very personal book Karen has opened her heart and her life to talk about the frequently unmentionable. In the process of sharing this very intimate account Karen has provided a point of contact for couples who may otherwise have felt very alone and isolated in their pain and loss.

The spiritual insights which she gained and which

she expresses, may help to provide a positive building block on which to move forward.

The loss of a pregnancy is the loss of dreams and hopes and possibilities, and the loss of a child that has been very real and yet hidden. This book is a personal account and experience, and others may have experienced the same event in a different way. However, there are many common threads which will be helpful to others in a similar situation. I am glad that Karen took the courage to write this book. If you have suffered similarly I hope that in reading it you may be touched and helped.

EILEEN BAILDAM,
Consultant Paediatrician, University of Salford School of Medicine

CHAPTER ONE

My miscarriage
— the pain had just begun

I WAS TWELVE weeks pregnant and, for the third week in a row, our family doctor was trying to detect a heart beat with a special instrument. We were both straining to hear something, anything, above the throbbing gushing of my own circulation. I must admit, I was excited at the prospect of being able to hear the sounds of life; some tangible evidence of my baby, other than this constant, wearing nausea.

The doctor tried again and again, sliding his probe over my skin.

'No, Karen,' he said, 'I'm afraid we still can't pick up anything. But don't worry, it's early days yet. Just make another appointment for next week, and we'll see what we can find.'

I drove home. I remember feeling vaguely apprehensive. But excited too. We were living in Chicago at the time. Bernie, my husband, was finishing his higher degree in Theology. It was fun living in an apartment block where we were all seminary families. All of us at the end of our training, virtually all of our husbands sure of a job to go to, and seven of us pregnant, relieved that we would no longer have to support our spouses!

Bernie wasn't there when I got home. I really only saw him in the mornings before I went off to work. I wasn't going to be alone though. Most of the wives were coming round to our place to discuss getting together every week for a chat and craft night, as we were all pretty much on our own in the evenings. Eventually, and inevitably the conversation came around to babies, and due dates, and such, and I waited for the right moment to share our special secret. It was thrilling, and wonderful to feel the warm bonds of womanhood that drew us closer together as we marvelled at the mystery of motherhood.

Somehow the implications of those tense moments in the surgery hadn't sunk in. Coming from England, and having no previous experience of maternity procedures, it did seem pretty early to try and detect a heartbeat, anyway. Somewhere in my mind I remembered sixteen weeks as being the time for finding a heartbeat with a stethoscope. So I wasn't really too worried, and I'd made it past twelve weeks, so I thought the danger of miscarriage had past. Besides, I'd never really heard of anyone having a miscarriage, so they must be pretty rare, too. There were some small nagging doubts, but more about the health of the baby, than anything else.

Next morning I grovelled into work. Dear God, I prayed, please take this nausea away! I can barely concentrate on my clients. All my other pregnant friends are blooming like June roses, and I feel like a foggy February! I can think of no useful reason why pregnant women should feel so dreadful! And why all day too? This is certainly not just 'morning' sickness!

Please may it stop now that I've made it past the first three months. Please!

I wobbled into the occupational therapy department of the small rehabilitation clinic where I worked. Diane, my assistant, fetched me a glass of water. She knew I'd been to the doctor's again. 'Did you hear anything this time?'

'No', I said. 'But it's all right. I guess it's just a bit early.'

'Aren't you worried? I would be! Are you sure everything's all right? You've been awfully stressed recently.'

'Oh, I'll be fine once this nausea's lifted. Come on, Pete will be here for his session soon.' Another busy day.

Wednesday. Work as usual. Till mid-morning. Then I noticed I was beginning to spot blood. Next time I looked there was a bit more. I tried to call Bernie between his lectures, hoping he'd have to go back to the apartment for something.

'Bernie, I'm spotting blood! Please call the doctor for me. I don't know what to do! I don't think I can make it home on my own. I'm beginning to feel really weak and strange. But I've got to try and stick it out here. I don't want a big panic! Only Diane knows I'm pregnant anyway!'

Bernie called back. 'Our doctor wasn't there. But his partner says to take it easy, go to bed, and take paracetamol if you're in pain. Oh, and if anything happens, we've got to collect everything solid. Look darling, I'll meet you from work, and I'll try and get the evening off.'

I don't know how I made it through that day. I

think Diane took some of my clients. She was really worried about me. By the time Bernie arrived, I was in a state of shock.

We drove home. We spent the evening close together, trying to cope with what was to come, but never imagining how traumatic it would be. I had never thought of miscarriage as anything more than a heavy period. I'd never really considered the emotional aspects of such a loss. Already this child within had been named: Matthew or Sarah. Already the baby was a reality to me; not just a mass of cells, or even a foetus: it was our child. Already I had dreams for the future. . . . But now everything was slipping helplessly from us, from me. We sat alone in the dark, waiting, praying, crying, losing blood. Eventually we went to bed.

Sleep didn't come easy as we lay there in each other's arms. And when it came, it was brief. I woke at two o'clock with a strange ache that came and went in gentle waves. I just lay there feeling it come and go, hardly daring to move. I was in a mini-labour. It became more and more intense. I tried to remember what I'd read about breathing techniques, and tried them out, more to distract myself, than to ease the pain. Finally, I woke Bernie. 'Bernie, I'm in labour or something. What are we supposed to do?'

'The doctor said there was no need to go to hospital or anything. He thought we should be able to manage on our own at home. Just remember to collect everything solid like he said. I'm here with you, we'll cope.'

'Lizzie downstairs is a nurse,' I said. 'I wish someone was here who'd know what to do. I just don't want to wake her in the middle of the night. Oh, Bernie, I'm so afraid. I can't believe this is happening!'

I kept feeling a need to push, and to use the bathroom. We spent the next hour running to the bathroom, Bernie with ladle and peanut-butter jar, trying to follow the doctor's orders, and retrieve whatever was solid from the toilet, but there was so much blood, he couldn't really see. Once I felt a sensation inside as if something was pulling away from me. I knew that that was goodbye. We saw some shapes through the glass. I held the jar, gazing at its contents. My child, I thought. There was more pain, getting worse. It wouldn't go away. I was scared. So much blood. Sitting in the bathroom I passed out. Bernie caught me and tried to hold me. In my semiconsciousness I thought he was throwing me around the room. I tried to scream.

When I was quiet again, I said, 'Bernie, I think we ought to go to Emergency. I'm scared. It seems to be all over now, but I hurt worse than ever.'

We drove to the nearest hospital. I was wheeled in, and laid on a bed. The nurse settled me down. Outside in the corridor I heard a junior doctor refer to me as 'the lady having an abortion'. He removed a piece of placenta that was left behind, and discharged me.

We drove home again. Empty. Barren. I was struggling to find something positive to cling to. Something to give me comfort and hope. We drove east, into the sunrise. Pink and yellow swirling into the night-blues; gold burning into the horizon. Bereaved of a child we had loved, but never held. A life we had made, but never seen. A baby that was real to us, but one we had never known. I began to say something about the dawn, and the promise of new beginnings, but it was bravado. I went home and cried. The pain was just beginning.

After we arrived home I washed and dressed slowly, as if in a daze. Then I telephoned work to tell them why I wouldn't be coming in. It was a Thursday morning, so I would take Friday off, too, and then the weekend, and I had to go back on Monday, as any extra days off would be unpaid, and we couldn't afford to lose that much money. We had invited guests for dinner over the weekend, and I decided not to put them off, because the distraction might be good for me. Bernie was given a couple of days off to be with me too.

News soon spread around our friends, and nearly every time I opened the door, there would be a little handful of flowers from someone's children; a loaf of home-made bread; a note or a card. Each little treat warmed my heart. Then a bouquet of flowers arrived from the clinic where I worked. Ironically, I had planned to break the news of my pregnancy to my boss on the Thursday that I miscarried, so many of my colleagues had no idea I was expecting a baby at all! But they were wonderfully kind and understanding.

One of the ladies we had to dinner that weekend had lost a baby twenty years before; a tiny foetus, that she had seen. She was the first person I had ever known who had had a miscarriage. She spoke of her thoughts about that tiny life, and how she believed that there would be a baby waiting for her when she arrived in heaven. I hadn't really reached that point in my thoughts about my own miscarriage. She was maternal and comforting, understanding, without being over-emotional.

As the days went by I had all kinds of questions, medical, philosphical and theological. Many of them without any concrete answers. I lived in fear that I may be called for a D&C operation (dilation and curettage), where my cervix would be dilated and my uterus scraped clean of anything left behind, to prevent infections and other problems. I prayed that the lab investigations at the hospital would show that the foetus and the placenta were all intact and had been completely removed. Besides, a D&C under general anaesthetic, even in day surgery, cost nearly as much at the local Chicago hospital as having a straightforward full-term baby delivered. It horrified me that it might cost as much to lose a baby at three months as it would to deliver a healthy baby full term. It seemed so ironic, and somehow rubbed salt in my emotional wounds.

A chaplain from the hospital sent me some information about miscarriages and emotional support. We chatted and she even suggested that once the foetus had been released from the labs, there may be a possibility of a free burial service. We'd never thought about that, and we never had the chance to make a decision, anyway.

I received a phone call. The lab tests had found the placenta and some massive blood clots, but no foetus. Then I realized: the foetus had probably been flushed away. This is something that I am still coming to terms with. Somehow I felt that I should have held the little form, at least, shown that I cared for it, even though it was tiny and dead.

My grief doubled with this information. There would be no burial now. But Bernie and I prayed together, and had our own service of farewell for the tiny fragment of life we had called ours.

We went to see our doctor, wondering whether he had decided to do a D&C. No, he said, I wouldn't need one, and a load of fear rolled away. He prayed with us, for the healing of our emotions, and for the well-being of a future pregnancy, and I really appreciated his sensitivity, his spirituality, and his warmth. It helped to heal some of the pain of the impersonal and clinical episode in the emergency room, which had left me feeling that the medical profession was dismissive and unsympathetic towards women losing their babies.

Our doctor said it would be best to wait three months before trying again, and I dared not risk another miscarriage experience. It seemed like a lifetime away before we could start over again, and I wondered how I would ever last so long! But we knew that in three months we would have to move back to England, and we'd be very busy anyway. We might as well wait until we were settled again in our new home. But the waiting time was hard.

CHAPTER TWO

Did God know my baby?

I SAT THERE in the church, two days after losing our baby, trying desperately hard to hold myself together. Friends kept passing by, and touching me, telling me they cared. Then there was a hymn. I forget which one it was, but it was about the Second Advent, and angels, and I think there was something about the resurrection. Whatever it was, I crumbled, sobbing heart-rending sobs, loudly on the back pew, at the end of the first church service. I wanted to go home, but Bernie had been asked to take part in the next service, and the pastor asked if he would go on the platform. 'No,' I said, 'please, I need him with me.' It was going to be an ordeal as it was, and, to make it even harder, our best friends were having their newly-adopted baby daughter dedicated that day.

We had had to move to the front of the church, so that Bernie could participate without having to be on the platform. I sat in the pew, flicking through my Bible. I had always been told that the Bible contained comfort for every situation. There must be something about miscarriage. Yes, there were wonderful Old Testament passages declaring they were the result of disobeying God's laws. Bitter signs of God's anger. Not exactly comforting! I wept angry tears. 'God, speak to me! I know you're there! I know you must have something to say about the loss of our baby! Do you care about this precious bud of life, or was it just another mass of disposable cells, like so many others seem to think? You gave the life in the first place! Does that mean anything to you? Or did you tear the child from me to punish me? There's plenty of reasons why you could have done that! See? I've been punished, does it make you feel any better, and what am I supposed to do now?'

The angry thoughts shocked my soul as my broken heart spat them out in hot tears. As a child I remember once pouring lashings of loneliness onto my adored teddy. At the end of it all I sat, quiet, waiting for some comfort. But nothing came. Teddy just sat there staring at me with her little glassy eyes (it was a 'she' teddy!), unmoved by my passionate soliloquy. Frustrated by her inadequacy, I picked her up and dashed her against the wall, only to be filled with love and remorse once she lay upside-down again on the carpet. And now I felt I could do the same with my Bible, but foresight told me it would only lead to greater remorse this time.

The Psalms. Must be something there. That's where all the feelings are. But then, David never had a miscarriage, what would he know about such emotions? There again — he had lost a son shortly after birth. It took a while to arrive at the right place, but it was there, almost at the end, a chapter that causes me to marvel, even now, at its appropriateness. God hadn't let me down. He led me to the perfect passage of comfort to show how much He cared. Psalm 139.

> 'O Lord, you have searched me and you know me.
> You know me when I sit and when I rise;
>   you perceive my thoughts from afar.

You discern my going out and my lying down;
    you are familiar with all my ways.
Before a word is on my tongue
    you know it completely, O Lord.
You hem me in, behind and before;
    you have laid your hand upon me.
Such knowledge is too wonderful for me,
    too lofty for me to attain.
Where can I go from your Spirit?
    Where can I flee from your presence?
If I go up to the heavens, you are there;
    if I make my bed in the depths, you are there.
If I rise on the wings of the dawn,
    if I settle on the far side of the sea,
even there your hand will guide me,
    your right hand will hold me fast.
If I say, "Surely the darkness will hide me
    and the light become night around me,"
even the darkness will not be dark to you;
    the night will shine like the day,
    for darkness is as light to you.
For you created my inmost being;
    you knit me together in my mother's womb.
I praise you because I am fearfully and wonderfully made;
    your works are wonderful, I know that full well.
My frame was not hidden from you
    when I was made in the secret place.
When I was woven together in the depths of the earth,
    your eyes saw my unformed body.
All the days ordained for me were written in your book
    before one of them came to be . . . .
Search me, O God, and know my heart;
    test me and know my anxious thoughts.
See if there is any offensive way in me,
    and lead me in the way everlasting.'
                (Psalm 139:1-16, 23, 24, NIV.)

First, in this psalm, God tells me that whatever I do, He knows about it. He knows about our loss, He knows about my tears. He knows about my thoughts, even before I think them (verse 2)! So God is aware of all that I'm going through right now. Then, in verses 7-12, He tells me there is nowhere I can go to hide from Him. He was there at the rehab centre when I began to spot. He was there in the bathroom when we lost the baby. He was holding my hand through the pain of the emergency room, and He's still here now, holding me in His arms, grieving with me, because He never intended life to be like this.

God has made us all wonderfully. Marvellous are His works (verse 14), including me. I am no less wonderful for having had a miscarriage. I don't have to feel inadequate or second rate, because I couldn't carry my own child to term. And my Creator, the source of all life, knows even the moment 'in secret' (verse 15) when conception took place, even though we weren't at all aware of it! He saw the child growing inside me (verse 16), and all its days were already known, even before any of them were truly lived! So God was aware of that brief life, and all its tiny movements.

Was the miscarriage a result of some historic sin I had committed? No. I don't believe so. Earlier, in Psalm 103, David tells us that:

> 'He does not treat us as our sins deserve
> or repay us according to our iniquities.
> For as high as the heavens are above the earth,
> so great is his love for those who fear him;
> as far as the east is from the west,
> so far has he removed our transgressions from us.
> As a father has compassion on his children,
> so the Lord has compassion on those who fear him;

> for he knows how we are formed,
> he remembers that we are dust.'
> (Psalm 103:10-14, NIV.)

God loves me! He is not a vindictive avenger, but a compassionate parent, gentle with my frailties.

I believe that God cares about all life, however small and apparently insignificant. I believe that 'all things work together for good to them that love God'. (Romans 8:28.) At the day of resurrection, there will be many happy reunions, and if it is best for me, and right for our child, I believe that God could be waiting there with my unknown baby. But many things are hidden from us now. Whatever is in store for us in heaven, I know it will be the most wonderful place we could ever be, full of happy surprises, and 'God shall wipe away all tears from (our) eyes; and there shall be no more death, neither sorrow, nor crying, neither shall there be any pain'. (Revelation 21:4.)

As I thought about these things over a few days, and even weeks, I began to feel comfort. I could feel the touch of a caring God through all my pain, soothing the hurt out of my slowly healing heart. I began to smile again, to trust more deeply in a God who had not left me alone and misunderstood through the greatest trauma of my life. He had been there. He was big enough to turn all my 'Why?'s into a deeper relationship with Him, unthreatened by my angry tears, unshakeable. I realized that God loved me and understood me in this the most secret of feminine sorrows. Sometimes I've felt that when David was inspired to write Psalm 139, God already knew how much comfort it would bring to me, thousands of years later! I love Him all the more for knowing that He never let me down, even at this most crucial moment of my life.

CHAPTER THREE

What has happened to me?

AFTER THE initial shock of my experience, I began to wonder what had happened and why? I knew very little about the subject. The only person I had heard of who had ever had a miscarriage was a very distant acquaintance of my mother. She had had several miscarriages and finally had a very premature baby that had nearly died. I felt that miscarriage must be extremely rare, and happened only to women with something particularly wrong with them. I began to wonder what was so wrong with me that I should have had one too.

When I began to find out the facts, I was quite surprised! Although it is generally accepted that at least one in every ten pregnancies ends in a miscarriage, some statistics indicate that the loss rate could be as high as one in five — with many miscarriages occurring even before the mother is aware of a pregnancy. I could hardly believe there were so many, when I had virtually never heard of it happening. Later I realized that many mothers hide the sorrow inside themselves and never talk about it, because they have found that most people don't understand their feelings and reactions. Then, when someone else mentions their own sad experiences, they suddenly become free to share what has lain so long in their own hearts, their pain, their memories, their lonelinesses, and the experience of being misunderstood.

So I learnt that what had happened to me wasn't so rare after all. Maybe I wasn't the freak person I had initially seen myself as. But I still needed to know what had happened to my body and my baby. Had I done something to cause the loss of our baby? This was an important question as I grappled with my own sense of guilt and grief.

I discovered that it is seldom anything a mother has done that will cause a miscarriage. Many miscarriages happen because the baby has failed to develop normally, and this is nature's way of coping with such an abnormality. In studies, up to 60 per cent of the miscarried foetuses had some form of abnormality, such as Down's syndrome, spina bifida, anencephaly (where the baby develops without a brain) or heart defects. It is still not known why some of these babies miscarry, and others are born and survive, but about 70 per cent of Downs syndrome pregnancies are lost through miscarriage. The miscarriage of an abnormal foetus usually happens earlier, rather than later in pregnancy. Chromosomal abnormalities, such as Down's syndrome, are often chance occurrences, and very rarely the result of a strong hereditary factor, so the risk of it happening again in a future pregnancy is very slim. Sometimes the fertilized ovum fails to develop normally, or implant properly, and so miscarries.

There are miscarriages where the baby is perfectly normal, but there is some kind of maternal abnormality which impedes the pregnancy. The uterus may be 'double', with two chambers, or irregularly shaped, or fibroids may develop within the uterus. All these may limit the space available for the foetus to grow in, and a miscarriage may occur. In an ectopic pregnancy, the fertilized egg stays in the fallopian tubes and doesn't enter the uterus. These tubes are quite narrow and soon burst during the early weeks of pregnancy if the embryo begins to develop there. This can be extremely dangerous, as internal bleeding occurs, and must be treated surgically as soon as possible. The foetus is removed and the damaged tube repaired or sealed off. An ectopic pregnancy is very painful, and you would certainly be aware that something was wrong.

Sometimes a mother can become ill in pregnancy and this can cause a miscarriage. I had a second miscarriage, at six weeks, after developing flu. High fevers, viruses and kidney infections can sometimes kill the foetus. But if the pregnancy continues safely through such an illness, the baby is unlikely to be harmed as a result. German measles is known to be harmful to the baby if the mother suffers with it during her pregnancy, which is why it is so important to be sure you are immune to it before becoming pregnant. Listeriosis has also received a lot of publicity recently, as the mother's illness can harm the unborn child. Now pregnant women are advised not to eat 'cook-chill' foods, and certain unpasteurized and soft cheeses, which may carry the listeria bacteria. Listeria can also be picked up from soil, raw vegetables which have been inadequately washed, and some animal faeces. Toxoplasmosis is a disease that may be carried in raw meat, or by a cat that is a carrier. Toxoplasmosis can cause foetal brain damage, blindness, malformation of the head, or fatal illness. It is best to avoid raw meat (wash your hands well after touching any), and handling cats, especially their faeces. If you have a cat, you can have it tested for toxoplasmosis, and have it immunized by a vet.

Hormone deficiencies can be a cause of problems. This was why, when I became pregnant for a third time, my consultant ordered extra injections of hormone (known as HCG) for the first fourteen weeks. But first he checked the viability of the foetus with an ultra-sound scan. There was no way of knowing whether this played a part in helping the pregnancy to be maintained, and there are still uncertainties as to the long-term effects on the child of such treatment. It helped me feel more supported through the early, and vulnerable stages of my pregnancy. I was horribly sick while on the hormone treatment, and vowed I would never have it again, but I was even sicker during my next pregnancy, when I didn't have the hormone injections!

Large doses of drugs, anaesthetic gas, a malignancy, blood group incompatibility, sexually transmitted diseases, working with toxic substances, using alcohol, extreme stress, severe emotional shock, and extreme nutritional deficiencies have all been found to be possible causes of miscarriage.

Older mothers may be more likely to have a miscarriage, probably because there is a greater risk of abnormality with increasing age (of either parent, in point of fact).

Vitamin deficiencies, such as low levels of folic acid, can help increase the risk of miscarriage, maybe because the lack of this vitamin can be a factor in causing neural tube defects, such as spina bifida and anencephaly. Folic acid is found in green leafy vegetables. Vitamin C has also recently been found to be very important in the normal development of a foetus. It is much better to try and eat a good diet, high in fresh fruit, and green leafy vegetables, than to take vitamin supplements. But if you have a family history of spina bifida, or are too sick and nauseated to eat a proper diet, then your doctor may prescribe the vitamins you need.

Research is being done all the time, and new discoveries are being revealed about possible reasons for miscarriage. The Harris Birthright Centre for Early Pregnancy at St. Mary's Hospital, Paddington, London, has been using immunotherapy techniques to treat women who have had three or more miscarriages by the same partner. The special treatment has enabled nearly 80 per cent of women in their programme to have a full-term baby the next time around, although the exact immune responses causing the loss of a pregnancy have not yet been identified.* When considering special techniques like these it is important to consider that these treatments *may* allow babies to be born with defects and diseases that might otherwise have been naturally miscarried.

New research is also being done into the genetic causes of miscarriage. Blighted ova, which account for 20 per cent of all miscarriages, are being linked with such causes,* and various chromosomal studies are helping to find some answers.

Another study has highlighted the fact that 80 per cent of women who repeatedly miscarry also have

polycystic ovaries. Polycystic ovaries* may be linked
with higher than normal levels of luteinising hormone during the monthly cycle, something that has
been significantly linked with causing miscarriage.

There are, unfortunately, many reasons for miscarriage, and most of us can never discover the actual
reasons for our own losses. Virtually all the causes of
miscarriage are beyond our control, and are not there
to make us feel guilty. But if there is a problem with
repeated miscarriage, then some of the reasons and
the research may help you achieve a successful pregnancy in the future.

If you want to find out the latest information then
you can write to Well-Being (formerly called Birthright), a charity which funds medical research into
women, pregnancy, childbirth, and babies. (See Appendix.)

---

*These statistics are contained in studies published in the
1991 Birthright annual report.

CHAPTER FOUR

It hasn't really happened . . . has it?

AS WE drove back from the hospital, into the
pastel swirls of a late summer sunrise, we left
behind the remnants of our brief pregnancy. I felt a
strange mixture of emotions. Part of me felt strangely
high, euphoric, a feeling of lightness that could have
come from losing so much blood. As we arrived home
I entered a sort of miasma; a cloud over my feelings
as I tried to tackle some of the practicalities. Washing
my own blood out of the bedclothes and towels;
phoning work to say I wouldn't be in; explaining
what had happened to colleagues who didn't even
know I was pregnant; phoning our families; arranging time off studies for Bernie, so we could be
together. Mechanically I made breakfast, tidied up,
and prepared for our weekend guests. . . . I went
about it all in a daze. Each activity seemed to take
all my concentration, even though it didn't need to. I
moved slowly, as if in a haze. Sometimes I would
become quite bubbly and flippant. Sometimes I would
stop, and cry and cry.

I began to make exciting plans for my future, and
started looking for interesting jobs back home in
England. I shared some of my ideas with a friend,
and she became quite concerned, thinking that I was

looking at work beyond my capabilities. Whether that was true or not, it took several years to understand her reaction. I thought she was being discouraging. She probably wanted to keep me in touch with reality. The fact is that one wonderful dream had just been destroyed for me. I was looking forward to going home to England, settling down, and having a baby. Life had seemed perfect, all worked out, with a beautiful future. One dream had died, and I needed another. I don't know if I was being unrealistic or not about the job. That doesn't really matter. The fact is that I was seeking another dream, something to look forward to, another reason to go home to England and leave the most exciting career prospects I'd ever had behind me, in America. I needed something to hold on to; something to help me adjust to a broken future, and to help me mend a shattered world.

I even wondered whether the whole miscarriage experience was just a very vivid dream, and now I had woken up—still pregnant. I tried to convince myself there was still a baby inside me. Maybe I had had twins and just lost one of them, and there would still be a baby one day. For the first week or so all these things went through my mind, throwing me from one set of emotions to another.

Fortunately for us Bernie was attending a special class on grief recovery as part of his seminary studies. He was able to tell me about a pattern of emotions that happens after a loss, whether the loss was the death of a loved one, a miscarriage, a redundancy, a broken ambition or even the amputation of a limb. Whatever the loss, the cycle of emotions is usually similar. Each phase of the pattern will take a different length of time, depending on the nature of the loss, the individual concerned, and his own life experiences and beliefs.

The first phase is usually denial. 'This can't have happened to me!' 'He's not really dead! I won't believe it until I actually see him.' 'This is just a bad dream, and soon I'll wake up.' The shock of the reality of the situation can be too much for the mind to take in, and denial helps to cushion the body from the shock until it is ready to listen to the truth. Sadly, some people never get past denial, and lose contact with reality. Some women decide never to get pregnant again, so they will never experience the horror of another miscarriage.

The next stage is often anger. A person may be angry with their doctor, employer, or whoever may have seemed to cause the calamity. Often they may also be angry with God, because He seems to have 'let' the disaster happen without intervening. 'How could God let my child die? She had never done anything wrong in her life!'

There may be a time of bargaining. During this stage a person will try to bargain with God, and may say to Him things like, 'If I do such and such, then You won't let me have another miscarriage, will You?'

Then there comes guilt. 'If only I'd done this, or that, this never would have happened to me.' 'It's all my fault. I should never have let it happen.' 'Maybe this is a punishment for something awful I have done in the past.'

These first four stages can happen very quickly, in a matter of minutes. Sometimes it may take a few days or weeks to work through these stages. Often the stages overlap, or a person may fluctuate back and forth between the stages as they think over their tragedy. One thing is inevitable if there is to be a healthy recovery from grief, and that is a time of mourning and sadness. Sometimes a person may become stuck at one level of recovery for years, and become very angry, or guilty and depressed, destroying their relationships. It is helpful to be aware of the stages of grief recovery, and if you find yourself sticking at one level, to seek a good counsellor.

In most of the different cultures throughout the world there is a prescribed pattern of mourning. The grieving individuals may be confined to their home for a time, and friends and relatives come to be with them and cry with them. There are special routines and rituals to follow which can help to structure the life-style of the grieving person at a time when making choices and important decisions is a very difficult thing to do. Our Western culture does not have such a rigid pattern of rituals following the death of a person, and that can make it harder for us to cope at a time of terrific stress and emotional turmoil. There is also no pattern of behaviour set out for friends and relatives to follow, so they are often unsure what to do 'for the best'. Death has been described as one of our culture's last great taboos. We can talk about sex and religion and politics, and bodily functions, but not about death. In other societies death may be accepted as a normal part of life; in our culture it can be seen as a failure of medical and scientific technology; we have conquered virtually everything else — we can even fly to the moon, but we cannot prevent death. Also, in our culture we are taught that we can control our own destinies, make our own choices, seek our own goals, and death is something we have no power over, and so we become uncomfortable about it.

All these cultural factors make grieving a complicated task anyway. A miscarriage loss can be even more complicated than ever, though. The few rituals our society has — a funeral — a burial or cremation — wreaths of flowers — cards and letters — generally do not materialize to help us say farewell, and to surround us with the love and sympathy of our friends. There is no public recognition of the death of an unborn child, although some hospital staff are now becoming aware of the importance of this for the families involved.

If you miscarry in hospital, you can ask to see the baby. If you know the sex, it can be helpful to give the baby a name. These things may sound strange, and even morbid, but they can help you through the grieving process. In early miscarriage there is often not a lot to see, except for blood clots, and sometimes the sight of a tiny foetus can be distressing. The decision is yours, but most women who do see their baby are glad that they did.

You are free to choose to have your own special memorial service, if you wish. Bernie and I just had a brief time together, praying and thinking about our baby. You could plan a more involved service for you, your husband, and any other children you have. It is important to include them, however young, and explain what is happening in a way they can understand. Having a small ceremony like this need not involve others, yet it can give you all permission to grieve and say goodbye to your baby. If you want a more formal service, then the following guidelines may be helpful.

Having your own memorial service

If you would like to have your own small memorial service, consult the chaplain of your local hospital. Each hospital has its own system for coping with miscarried foetuses. More and more hospitals are realizing that any life, however brief, deserves a dignified departure. The chaplain will know about these procedures, and how he can help you. He may have some very good ideas of his own about planning a service, or it might be totally new to him. I have a few suggestions.

Firstly, you need to decide who you want to involve in this service. Make it small, and very personal, you, your husband, your own children, close friends and family, and those who have been particularly supportive of you through your miscarriage. You may also like to include your pastor as a possible participant in the service.

Secondly, you need to plan the service. Choose hymns that tell of Jesus' love for little children, or of our hope of a future life together in heaven.

Chapter two of this book may have some useful ideas for a sermonette, or special Bible readings.

Have prayers for comfort in your own grief, and for the comfort of all others suffering in a similar way. Pray for your future pregnancies, and for the hope you have that you may see your baby in heaven. Pray for the medical staff who care for those having miscarriages, that they will have wisdom, and be given special sensitivity towards the emotional needs of their patients. Pray for the researchers looking for answers as they study the problem of miscarriage, that they will discover useful information.

You might like to plant a tree in memory of your baby, or make a donation to a miscarriage support group.

Burial

You may wish to have a proper burial. A hospital can sometimes arrange this. Some hospitals are now installing special incinerators for the cremation of miscarried babies. Some also provide a grave site, and plot number. A proper cremation can cost about £50 through a funeral director, and you may receive the ashes. A full burial could cost about £200 with a grave and a plaque. For more information, and up-to-date costs, contact SANDS (The Stillbirth and Neonatal Death Society). (See Appendix.)

CHAPTER FIVE

I just feel like crying

'I CRIED WHEN I realized I was going to miscarry. I cried during the miscarriage. I cried after the miscarriage. The bouts of tears were interspersed with periods of numbness and euphoria. I barely knew what I would feel from one hour to the next. Someone pointed out that my hormones were as crazy as if I had actually given birth full term, a thought I'd not considered. It does take time for the body to return to its normal hormonal balance, and, although my periods returned a month after the miscarriage, I know it took another six months for them to settle completely. It was as if my body had to take nine months to see a pregnancy through, even if that pregnancy ended long before the due date. Other friends have said the same thing, especially if their miscarriage was after the first three months.

Whatever the reason, hormonal or reactive, the sadness was there. At first the crying was prolonged and quite frequent, and slowly the weeks absorbed the tears. Now, even six years later, tears can well up in my eyes whenever I'm reminded of the child we lost.

It's normal to be sad after a miscarriage. When you have lost a baby you hoped for, even if the hope only lasted a day, it can be an intensely traumatic experience. Many people still think that the earlier the miscarriage, the less intense the sorrow. This is not necessarily so. The sadness can be very similar to someone suffering a still birth, and yet even more difficult to resolve because there may be no body to see, and hold and grieve over. And it is good to cry. It is natural and therapeutic to mourn for the loss of an expected child, and it is important that no one robs you of the time and space to experience your own sorrow. It is helpful, though, if you have an understanding person with whom to share your times of sadness. Find someone who has the time to be with you while you cry; someone who won't have to run off to do something else. Choose someone you feel close to, your husband may be the best person, and it is wonderful if he can be there to hold you while you cry. But if he is not available find someone else you feel totally at ease with. You may need to prepare somebody for sharing your 'sad' times. Say, 'I feel a need to express some of my sadness about the loss of our baby. I might cry a lot. I don't know. I would just like you to be there with me so I am not alone. I may need you to hold me and comfort me. But please don't feel you need to stop me crying; and please don't tell me I shouldn't cry. It may take a few minutes or a few hours, but it would mean so much to me if you could share this time with me.'

Crying is so natural, but many people feel uncomfortable when others cry because they don't know what to do. A few minutes preparation can be helpful, because it allows you an opportunity to express your expectations, and relieve their embarrassment and discomfort. When your friend or husband is put at ease in this way, they may be better able to offer the support and comfort you really need. Husbands may be especially uncomfortable if they feel they ought to be crying for their lost child, but find they can't. These sorts of feelings can make him feel guilty, so be aware of his emotional needs too. He may need you to help him cope with his own medley of emotions, and they may be different to yours. That's all right. The important thing to remember is to use the experience to bring you both closer together, and not to let it push you apart.

Crying is often quite spontaneous during a time of grief. It may happen when you are quite alone, and there is nothing left to distract you from your feelings. It is fine to cry on your own too, but don't let it cause you to resent or blame your husband or friend for not being there when you need them.

Grief can make us quite irrational at times, and it can distort our perceptions of reality. If you find that in your sad times you are blaming others, or resenting them for their reactions to your grief, you may need to pause for a moment and think, 'Is this person deliberately trying to hurt me? Am I expecting too much from them? Have I tried to help them understand what I'm experiencing?' When we begin to find our thoughts disturbed by negative feelings towards those around us, we may need to ask ourselves some of these questions. Often we can get so overcome by our own sorrow we find it hard to think about those around us very clearly. Other people, however close, cannot be expected to read our minds, and they may have other things going on in their lives and experiences which make it hard for them to relate to you as fully as they would like.

About the time I miscarried our closest friends had discovered that the husband's mother was dying of cancer. I had never experienced what they were going through, and they knew very little about the emotional aspects of miscarriage. We had always shared all kinds of things together, and tried to support each other through the ups and downs of our lives. But now we were all quite deep in our own kinds of pain. Without taking time to discuss our experiences openly, we were still expecting each other to be more supportive than we were able to be. Negative feelings began to come between us and our friends which nearly destroyed a beautiful relationship, even though we each had some background in counselling and psychology. It has taken me six years to understand what was going wrong between us at that time, and to realize how I could have been more sensitive to my friends' needs. But I don't think I was fully aware of the intensity of my own emotions at the time, and I'm not sure I could have offered them much more support in my own grieving state. A little understanding would have gone a long way, though, and would have caused me fewer regrets later.

Crying is very healing. It is cathartic, and helps release our emotional energy. It can feel physically painful to hold back our tears, but a good sobbing session means we have to breathe deeply, and this helps us to feel refreshed and relaxed afterwards. There is nothing wrong with grief. Paul tells us that 'we do not want you to . . . grieve like the rest of

men, who have no hope.' 1 Thessalonians 4:13, NIV.
He does not say we are not to grieve, but reminds us
that in our grief we also have hope; we do not despair
in our sorrow, as those who have no eternal future to
look forward to.

When I first became pregnant I kept a diary of my
daily thoughts and emotions. I wanted to write a letter to the baby, too, to share with him or her one day.
I never got around to writing that particular epistle,
but this is one I wrote two months after the miscarriage, containing both the sorrow and the hope. It was
hard to write, and even now brings me to tears, but it
was one of the single most healing things I did during my recovery.

'Dear Matthew or Sarah,

'It's hard to write this letter now that you are
gone. All I feel is a great sense of loneliness where
you used to be, an aching emptiness. But before there
was the emptiness, there was you.

'It was very special to find out that, with God,
daddy and I had created you out of our love. We are
very much in love, and knowing that you grew as a
miracle from our love was something incredible and
wonderful. At first I could hardly believe that there
was a new life growing inside of me. You seemed so
tiny and fragile that I felt I might lose you, and not
even know about it. But, as time went on, my body
began to feel the changes that meant you were really
there.

'Your coming was a pleasant surprise, at least your
conception was. But we could see how God's plans
seemed more perfect than ours: how I could stay
home with you, and spend more time working with

your daddy. I wanted you so much. I was scared something would tear you away from me, or that one day I'd wake up and find that I had only been dreaming.

'I did have dreams, but they were of you, and you had beautiful auburn hair, and a sweet smile. Sometimes you were Matthew, sometimes Sarah. I had no clear ideas as to what you would look like, or what talents you would have. I just wanted you to learn how to love others, how to listen to others, how to have the right balance of self-confidence, and how to love Jesus with all your heart. You would bring us so much joy as we watched you grow and develop, listening to your funny sayings, sharing your happiness and hurts, growing together as a family . . .

'We were expectant as we visited the doctor to hear your heart beat—the first sound we would hear of your life. But there was only silence. Again I went alone, and still there was only silence when there should have been the gentle rhythms of your heart. I was scared, and wondered if you might be developmentally delayed, or hurt in some way. I wanted you to be whole and well. Something inside me cried so hard that night, though I didn't want to admit it. The next night something in me died.

'It was hard to lie there and let you go. I felt so helpless. I wanted you. I wanted to know you, to hold you in my arms, hear your voice, see your smile, watch you grow. Instead, I was watching you die before you had hardly begun; before we even knew, or could tell if you were Matthew or Sarah. For some strange reason I felt totally rejected by you. I felt I had given so much of myself and my heart to you, and you were just throwing it all back in my face, and walking out. I know it was not your fault, but I felt you couldn't love me, didn't need me. I was angry, hurt and violated. I felt you tear from my body, and you fell away before we could even catch you and hold you, and we never saw you. We could never cuddle you and say goodbye properly. Instead there was emptiness, tears and fears.

'I was never so sad in my life, and I've had other losses to cry over. You were part of me, and yet I had no control over losing you. I was totally helpless, and felt I had been a lousy mother, and not given you the best environment for growth. I felt a complete failure. I had failed you even before you were born. I had failed at my first opportunity of being a mother—anyone could have babies—it seemed—except me. Everyone around was doing it so easily.

'Now I'll never know you, not here on this earth. I don't know what heaven holds. Maybe one day an angel will hand me a baby to hug, and it will be you, and you'll bring me all the promised happinesses. Imagine! I could have a baby without the sleepless nights, and you would never feel the pain of teething, or the discomfort of colic or nappy (diaper) rash! Jesus only knows, and He loves you even more than we do. He cries with us in our loss. He doesn't want anyone to die. But this world has imperfections, and one of them is death. Heaven is perfect. And maybe you'll be there, and you'll never have to know all the hurts and sadnesses that exist on earth. You'll never know me as an imperfect mother, only as a perfect one.

'I want you to know that you were loved and wanted, more than you can probably comprehend. We feel very lonely without you. Each Easter (you were to be born at Easter-time) we will remember how our Easter chick never hatched. We will also remember how, at Easter, Jesus destroyed the power of death, and gave us hope. It is that hope we have now, because there are so many things about heaven we'll never know until we arrive. And whatever heaven holds, it will be wonderful.

'We love you, and hope to see you then.

'Mummy and Daddy.

x x x '

CHAPTER SIX

Why do I feel so guilty?

ONCE MY heart had let my mind come to the realization that our baby was gone, and the denial faded into fact, one of the hardest phases began to envelope me: guilt.

My mind kept rehearsing the question: Did I do something wrong that hurt the baby? There were a dozen or so 'maybe . . . ' answers. Maybe one of the tablets that I had been taking on prescription had had a damaging effect on the baby's development. I had been taking the tablets periodically to help quell the nausea from a minor medical problem, and I had taken a few around the time of the conception. Maybe they could have done the damage to our baby? I pondered this one night as I lay trying to sleep.

The next day I dragged out an enormous book from the library at work, and spent my lunch break poring through its pages. It was an encyclopaedia of drugs, and their side effects. For each drug it stated whether or not it would have a detrimental effect on a foetus. For my specific medication it said that so far there were no known effects on the developing foetus. At least it didn't say there were definitely risks for the foetus, but I could not relieve my guilt on something the medical world had not yet proven. If only. . . . If only. . . . My nausea was nothing compared to the loss of our child. If I had known I would become pregnant, I would not have taken any tablets to try and relieve my discomfort. If I hadn't taken them, I would have had no cause to feel guilty.

What else had I done? Oh, yes. A few days before I miscarried we had taken the clinic's clients out to play crazy golf. It had ended up being the hottest day of the whole year, even though it was September. For a whole afternoon I had suffered the intense heat, and I'd forgotten to take any money for a drink. In the evening Bernie and I had gone to a meeting in a school. It was so hot, and I couldn't settle. My body felt so strange and uncomfortable. I kept going out and splashing myself with cold water, and walking around. I felt so weird I couldn't even sit down, and wandered about outside until the evening cooled. Maybe the effects of the heat had damaged the baby? I could never know.

Maybe I hadn't eaten the right diet. Maybe I'd not eaten the right vitamins. Maybe I'd been under too much stress, or taken too much strenuous exercise.

Maybe the miscarriage was a punishment from God for my numerous sins. God knows there had been plenty of those.

And maybe I had been praying the wrong prayer. Bernie and I belonged to a special prayer group that met on Saturday evenings. We would take it in turns to present a prayer request, and then someone else in the group would choose to pray for each request, so everyone had a different person praying for them. The weekend before I miscarried, my special prayer request was that my nausea and sickness would subside. I was beginning to feel so ill I could barely work, and if I lost my job, we would have no income. Russell prayed for me. He was a gentle-natured person, very sensitive to other's feelings and needs. He prayed for me in a beautiful way though, as a bachelor, he had had no experience of anything to do with pregnancy. As the prayer group broke up, he promised me he'd continue to pray throughout the week, and he was sure God would answer our prayers, and my sickness would end.

Just a few days later I miscarried. The following Saturday evening we forced ourselves to go along to the prayer group again. Russell was eager to know if his prayer had been answered. Yes, it had. The pregnancy and the sickness had ended. We had lost the baby. The prayer group was shattered. The usual joy and peace we found there dissolved as we each tried to struggle with the implications of our prayers and requests. Maybe my selfish prayer request had caused our baby to die.

True guilt comes after we wilfully disobey the will of God. I know of no occasions when a miscarriage has actually been caused by a wilful, determined act of the mother. Usually the mother has been trying to do the best for the health of the baby: trying to eat healthfully, taking exercise, etc., and all of these are good things. I hadn't known I would conceive when I was taking the tablets. I believed I was doing the best for my body at that time. When we prayed for the relief of my 'morning sickness' we felt we were following God's desires that we should pray for healing when we are sick. None of these things are wrong. It's only when a miscarriage occurs that we look back to find reasons, and we find we have regrets, and begin to blame ourselves, because there does not seem to be any other reason for our loss.

One doctor tried to put things in perspective. He said, 'If exercise, or vitamins, or summer heat, or anything else, would cause a miscarriage, then there would be very few teenage pregnancies. A girl would go out and jump around until she lost the baby. And if you were worried about your stress levels before you miscarried, there can't be a much more stressful circumstance than being a pregnant teenager!' The chapter on the physical reasons for miscarriage may help you understand some of the reasons why miscarriages occur, that are completely beyond our personal control.

The problem with false guilt is that it tries to separate us from God. It also tries to present God in a false way, so that we are tempted to lose our trust in Him. When we are questioning and suffering we need God more than ever. Instead of becoming overwhelmed by our own situations, and trying to guess at what part God might be playing in our personal crises, it is comforting to look at just who God is. There are so many questions we cannot answer, and yet we can wreck our faith and happinness over them, rather than looking at the kind of God He truly is.

Psalm 103 is a wonderful psalm when we need to remind ourselves what God is really like. He isn't there to make us feel guilty; it's not His job to be our Accuser, but our Comforter.

Psalm 103, NIV.

'Praise the Lord, O my soul;
   all my inmost being, praise his holy name.
Praise the Lord, O my soul,
   and forget not all his benefits.
He forgives all my sins
   and heals all my diseases;
he redeems my life from the pit

and crowns me with love and compassion.
He satisfies my desires with good things,
   so that my youth is renewed like the eagle's.
The Lord works righteousness and justice
   for all the oppressed.
He made known his ways to Moses,
   his deeds to the people of Israel:
The Lord is compassionate and gracious,
   slow to anger, abounding in love.
He will not always accuse,
   nor will he harbour his anger for ever;
he does not treat us as our sins deserve
   or repay us according to our iniquities.
For as high as the heavens are above the earth,
   so great is his love for those who fear him;
as far as the east is from the west,
   so far has he removed our transgressions from us.
As a father has compassion on his children,
   so the Lord has compassion on those who fear him;
For he knows how we are formed,
   he remembers that we are dust.
As for man, his days are like grass,
   he flourishes like a flower of the field;
the wind blows over it and it is gone,
   and its place remembers it no more.
But from everlasting to everlasting
   the Lord's love is with those who fear him,
   and his righteousness with their children's
      children —
with those who keep his covenant
   and remember to obey his precepts.
The Lord has established his throne in heaven,
   and his kingdom rules over all.
Praise the Lord, you his angels,
   you mighty ones who do his bidding, who obey
      his word.
Praise the Lord, all his heavenly hosts,
   you his servants who do his will.
Praise the Lord, all his works

everywhere in his dominion.
Praise the Lord, O my soul.'

This is a beautiful psalm, where David describes the character and love of God. Read it through again, if you like, and pencil in the following descriptions of God next to the appropriate verses:

> Eternally loving
> Completely forgiving
> Guilt dissolving
> Understanding
> Tenderly compassionate
> Full of blessings
> Healing
> Redeeming
> Strengthening
> Gentle father

As you read, add more notes of your own, remember the different ways He has revealed His character to you, personally, in the past. Praise Him for the love and blessings He has shown you in the past, and pray that your present feelings of regret will be healed.

Some women are riddled with guilt because, for whatever reason, they may have had an abortion in the past, and they feel their miscarriage is a direct punishment for taking the life of a previous baby. Psalm 103 (NIV) says 'he does not treat us as our sins deserve,' and 'he remembers that we are dust' and fragile. 'He forgives all (our) sins' and only wants to shower us with His love and blessings. If a past abortion has been a problem for you, you may need to pray for forgiveness, and thank God that you have been forgiven, and recognize that He loves you. You may find that you need counselling to help you over the difficult emotional effects of having an abortion. If so, then try to find a trained Christian counsellor you can trust.

Some mothers can feel guilty after a miscarriage because they had resented their pregnancy all along. Babies don't always come at precisely the right moment, and an unexpected pregnancy can put a halt to an exciting career, disrupt study and travel plans, be yet another mouth to feed and another few years of intense mothering. Parenthood is not always a happy prospect, viewed from this perspective, and it is not difficult to resent an unwanted pregnancy. Negative feelings towards the baby and the pregnancy can induce guilt, especially after a miscarriage. The mother may be made to feel worse by well-meaning friends and relatives feeling sorry for her after her loss, when she has the mixed feelings of relief and remorse. The feelings of relief come from the natural end of an unwanted pregnancy, but the mother can also feel guilty that her negative feelings may have somehow caused the miscarriage, and that she somehow 'wished' the baby away, and is responsible for its death.

These feelings are a natural part of the grieving process, and need to be worked through. But it is worth remembering something else that the aforementioned doctor said, 'If an unwanted pregnancy could miscarry because the mother wished it to, then there would not be any need for abortions and many teenage pregnancies. Our bodies just don't work like that. It's our emotions working without a framework of reality that may cause us to believe we have wished a baby away.'

Feelings of guilt, for whatever reason, are like a heavy weight on our minds. Jesus says, '"Come to me, all you who are weary and burdened, and I will give you rest. Take my yoke upon you and learn from me, for I am gentle and humble in heart, and you will find rest for your souls."' Matthew 11:28, 29, NIV. Only Jesus can help us to feel better, and there is nothing He'd rather do than to give us peace of mind.

The second time I miscarried the guilt feelings were not nearly as strong, and a timely bout of flu helped with the grieving process. I had only just realized I was pregnant, and had very little time to become emotionally involved in the experience. I was starting a new job. The first day I felt strange, but thought that it was just the stress of getting back into the routine of a full day's work, and finding my way around a new hospital. At lunch time I felt a gush, and blood was pouring from me. I was shattered. I phoned Bernie in floods of tears, and tried to gather myself. I couldn't tell anyone at work what was happening. I existed in a cloud until it was time to go home.

At home I crumbled in a heap of depression. I just remember sitting on the sofa, unable to do anything, numb from inexpressible grief. I finally managed to find the energy to go to bed, and woke up the next morning feverish and ill with the flu. For some reason I couldn't summon up the will to do anything except lie in bed. I just felt desolate. All my questions about miscarriage had already been answered, and so

all I seemed to feel was an intense grief that im-
mobilized me for several days. The flu was a godsend.
It allowed me to curl up in bed and do nothing except
grieve. My heart and body healed together, freed from
external responsibilities. I felt even more strongly
that I'd never have a baby. But I had to get up and
go back to work, so that helped to distract me
somewhat. I was prone to fits of tears, and the feeling
that I'd never have children. But the next month I
conceived again.

CHAPTER SEVEN

Why do I feel so angry?

'**B**Y THE way, did you know that Amanda's pregnant?' A friend mentioned this fact quite casually a few weeks after our loss. 'Oh, no! Not another one! It seems like everyone can have babies except me!' The bitter tones in my voice surprised me. We were on our way to church at the time, and all through the services I chewed the information over in my mind. I did not want to see Amanda. I only knew her by sight, anyway. I found myself almost hating her for her ability to conceive. Inside I was all twisted up with vicious emotions and thoughts not compatible with a loving Christian attitude. I was appalled at the intensity of my feelings. I didn't feel like this towards all the other pregnant women at the institute, and I'd never even spoken to Amanda. But I was furious about her pregnancy. For some apparently inexplicable reason I felt it wasn't fair. If I couldn't have a baby, then neither should she.

Up until this point in time the only anger I'd felt in response to the miscarriage had been focused towards the unknown doctor who'd told Bernie I should 'collect everything solid, and take painkillers if it hurts'. I had been angry with him for his lack of responsiveness, and the practical uselessness of his advice. I'd also felt angry towards the Emergency room staff for referring to me as 'the lady having an abortion', and their apparent insensitivity to my emotions.* But I hadn't felt bad about those angers, and it hadn't screwed me up inside like this irrational anger towards another woman, who just happened to be pregnant.

A week or so went by, and many other things came to fill my mind. The intense anger subsided. And then another casual remark came my way. 'Amanda's just lost her baby, did you know?'

I'd felt bad enough about the awful feelings I'd had towards her, and now I felt guiltier than ever!

Our husbands realized we could have something to offer each other, and one Sunday evening they arranged for us to meet. Amanda and I talked for several hours about our own unique, and yet similarly painful, experiences. We shared all our thoughts and ideas about what had happened to us, and how it had affected us emotionally, physically and spiritually. It was a very healing time for me, though it was naturally difficult to go back and relive some of the things all over again in my mind.

Amanda's experience had been a little different to mine. My pregnancy, although welcome, was not really planned, but Amanda had been planning for four years, since her marriage, to become pregnant in that September when her husband was nearly through Seminary. She'd always wanted a June baby. She was delighted to conceive just as she had planned, but the miscarriage, within a couple of weeks of a positive pregnancy test, came as a tragic blow, her sense of disappointment even greater than my own.

We talked about how we had turned to our Bibles to find some grain of comfort, but looking up the word 'miscarriage' had uncovered even more pain. Nearly every reference to miscarriage in the Bible is associated with a punishment from God, and a curse, which is not exactly encouraging. In fact, such texts can lead to even more guilt and sadness at a very traumatic time.

But the greatest healing of that evening was finding that we were not alone in our thoughts and sorrows. There were other women out there who had had similar experiences to ourselves, who asked themselves the same questions we had: 'Why has this happened? Why has it happened to me? Does God care? What has happened to my baby? Why do I feel this way? Will I ever have a child?'

During this experience with Amanda the anger and resentment I had had towards her rapidly dissolved, and so did some of my feelings of isolation, the feeling that there was no one else I knew who had gone through what I was experiencing, and therefore no one who really understood. Frustration can lead to anger, and I had obviously been frustrated that she was pregnant when I was not. And jealous too.

Anger, resentment and loneliness are all quite natural emotions that can follow a miscarriage. As with the other stages of grief, they need to be worked through. If we let them fester for too long then the emotions can cripple and damage us as we try to relate to others, and ourselves.

If you begin to find you are feeling anger or resentment towards someone, a doctor, friend, relative or even your husband, you need to ask yourself 'why?' Is your anger irrational, or justified? Was the other person deliberately trying to hurt you, or were they trying to help you as best they could? Did you feel let down by someone you trusted? Did you feel misunderstood, or even insulted?

I was angry with the duty doctor for his inadequate advice to us. Now I know I should have gone to the Emergency department of the local hospital much sooner, rather than try and cope with a nightmarish situation at home, and his advice prevented us from wanting to bother the Emergency staff with something as apparently mundane as a miscarriage. I never met that doctor, but we explained to our own doctor that the advice we had been given about painkillers and collecting the 'solids' was not very helpful in the light of our own experience. Our doctor's practice gave every pregnant woman an information package about nutrition in pregnancy, local hospitals and their maternity care, and other useful leaflets. We suggested that they also include an envelope 'To Be Opened in Case of a Threatened Miscarriage', with information about the possible causes of miscarriage, and how to deal with the practical, emotional and spiritual issues surrounding such a trauma. A women suffering the physical and emotional trauma of a miscarriage needs to know what to expect, and how to deal with it.

Our doctor said he didn't like to worry women about the prospect of a miscarriage, but we said the sealed envelope idea would enable them to decide for themselves when and why they needed to read the information, and it was only fair to allow them that choice.

Your experience with your own doctor may be quite different, but if the way you were handled made you feel angry or uncomfortable, or you felt that you were given misleading information, then make an appointment to sit down and talk with him about it. Try and present your case calmly, and clearly, and listen to his perspective too. It won't help either of you if you rant and rave in the surgery, and he is much more likely to take notice if you talk to him in a rational, reasoned manner. You never know, you may help him to make things easier for another woman suffering a miscarriage, and your doctor may learn from the experience too. If you think your surgery needs a package to offer pregnant women that deals with miscarriage, try putting one together, using information from national and regional miscarriage organizations.

I never did speak to the Emergency room staff about referring to me as 'the woman having an abortion'. Now I wish that I had. Unfortunately this term is often used to describe women experiencing miscarriage.*

It is extremely painful to hear yourself being described as 'having an abortion' when you desperately wanted the baby, or if you abhor the idea of abortions, especially when your body is in the physical shock of a miscarriage. I believe that staff working with a miscarrying woman should avoid using this term, especially within earshot of the mother. Often they have been taught that this is the correct term to use, and that is fair enough, but it does no harm to tell them gently, 'I appreciate the reasons why you referred to me as having an abortion, but under the circumstances I don't feel it is appropriate. Most women who miscarry do not want to lose their baby, and when you refer to me as having an abortion it sounds as if you think that I wanted to lose this child. Please be sensitive to the emotional needs of your patients, and refer to them in a way that they can understand, and that does not increase their emotional pain.' You can say this face to face, or send a kind letter later, showing appreciation for your care but pointing out the need for sensitive language. More and more people who care for miscarrying women are aware of this issue, and are very good at helping them through the emotional trauma as well as the physical trauma, but Emergency room staff see all kinds of problems, and may not often come into contact with miscarriage.

Anger and resentment towards family members and friends needs to be resolved as soon as possible, so that important relationships can be restored and maintained. You need to identify the cause for your feelings, and this is sometimes hard to do in the heat of the moment. Ephesians 4:26 says, ' "In your anger do not sin". Do not let the sun go down while you are still angry.' The longer we leave an issue without sorting it out, the bigger it can become and the harder it is to deal with. You may feel that it is wrong to feel angry, but it is not the anger that is wrong, it is how we handle our anger that can be the problem. Moses was angry when he came down from the mountain to find the children of Israel worshipping the golden calf. He even smashed the tablets of stone with the Ten Commandments written on them. But God was not displeased with his behaviour because Moses had been right to be angry. Jesus drove the money-changers out of the temple because He was angry with their irreverence.

We have to pray and work out with God the real reasons for our angry feelings. If there has been a genuine injustice, then we can gently try to bring about a benefit to others, such as reminding the doctor that his well-intentioned advice was inadequate. If we are angry because our own needs haven't been met, or because we are frustrated, jealous, or feel misunderstood, then we may need to sit down and think of the best way to deal with the situation without causing pain to others.

As soon as you begin to realize that you feel angry or resentful towards someone else, pause and take time to examine your feelings and the reasons for them. Read through the chapters on husbands, relatives and friends. If they made an unthinking comment, see chapter eight and decide whether you want to respond or not. Most of your friends and relatives will be wanting to help you, not hurt you in any way, but they don't always know the best thing to do. They may find it easier to avoid you, or do nothing, rather than do something which might upset you.

It can be difficult when you are coping with a load of emotional pain yourself, but when you feel able you could tell people what you need from them. They will feel easier about relating to you if they know how you're feeling, or have something practical they can do to help you. Friends who have children and babies, or are pregnant, may feel that their presence will rub salt in your wounds. If you want to see them then you may need to invite them over, or make plans to go shopping together.

If you find that you cannot deal effectively with

any of your angry or resentful feelings, try to find someone to talk to such as a pastor, counsellor, or trusted friend. Sometimes we just need someone to listen while we express our emotions, or have a good pillow-thumping session to help release some of our pent-up emotional energy.

If you find yourself feeling angry towards God, try reading chapter two. Don't avoid God, but try to spend more time with Him. Talk to Him about how you feel; you may even like to try writing Him a letter, or keeping a diary of your 'conversations' with Him. Read about His love and compassion, using a concordance to help you find the texts, and write down the ones that mean most to you. Or find promises of His eternal caring, and make your own promise box. Although you may feel at a spiritual low now, it will be exciting to work through your relationship with God. You may find that you will grow into a new closeness with Him if you stick with Him, and trust Him not to let you down. It is wonderful to discover that you can trust God whatever comes your way, and out of that will grow a deepening peace with Him that will help you through any future challenges.

---

*'Miscarriage' is a lay term. Medically the premature delivery of a foetus before it is 'viable' is termed a 'spontaneous abortion'. Sensitive medical personnel accept that this term is unfortunate and that to abbreviate it to 'abortion' is even more so.

The time period covered by the term 'spontaneous abortion' varies from country to country. The World Health Organization definition extends to 28 weeks. Legally, in Britain, it is 24 weeks. In practice most would use it up to 18-20 weeks.

CHAPTER EIGHT

How do I cope with my friends' reactions?

NOW, WHEN I look back on our miscarriage experience, I see that the friends who responded in the most loving ways often didn't say anything at all! There was a loaf of home-baked bread on the doorstep; a beautiful set of underwear wrapped in tissue and lace that a friend had originally chosen for herself; a hug and some tears; a bouquet of flowers from my colleagues at work. These are the things I remember now. The underwear set helped me to feel feminine again, and it is something I will always treasure. As a friend, it is these little touches that mean so much when someone has lost a baby through miscarriage. A small gift, a well-chosen card, and a hug, all say you care, all say that you are sad too, all say that you are there, and often that is enough.

A friend may need to listen too, to a retelling of events, to questions and fears, to things that may touch painful chords in her own heart. One friend sobbed and sobbed over me a couple of days after our loss, and I had to try and comfort her. She was about to try for a baby, and the thought that a miscarriage could happen to her was unbearable. I just hugged her and let her cry. I wasn't going to say, 'Don't worry, it won't happen to you!'; I had heard that myself several times during my own short pregnancy!

To be honest I don't think I would have known what to say if any of my friends had come to me having experienced a miscarriage. I think it would have been all too simple to come out with the same pat phrases I heard after my own miscarriage. They are easy words to say, that comfort the speaker more than the listener, and fill in the discomfort of not knowing what else to do. So I don't blame them for what they said. The fact that they said anything at all meant that they were trying to let me know they cared, and that they wanted to show they cared in a tangible way. Too often, though, the 'simple' answers after a miscarriage throw up a whole complexity of thoughts and emotions, and may even say dangerous things about God.

'Well, you can always have another baby.'

Can I have another baby? I thought I could have this one, and now it has gone. And, anyway, no other baby will ever replace this one that I have lost. Each child is a unique individual. It is the loss of never being able to know this child that I miscarried that makes me feel so sad. And who knows, maybe I will be one of those people who can never have a child, who continually miscarries. It does happen. I may have already been trying for months to conceive the child we have just lost. The thought of starting over again, although I want to, fills me with apprehension and I feel demoralized.

'Just forget about this baby and have another as quickly as possible.'

I can never forget this baby. It was a part of me. It

had become a part of my future, as well as my 'now'. It is never easy to forget any child, a mother just isn't made that way. No matter how apparently insignificant that life may have been to others, it has been very special to me. I don't want to forget my child. I hope the memories of the loss will heal in time and be less painful than they are now, but the child will always be my child. I need time and space to grieve, and my body and heart may need time to heal before it is wise to think about trying for another baby.

'It was only a blob of cells, it's easier if you don't think of it as a baby.'

We are all just masses of cells. It is not the size of the mass that makes us more or less important. Each life is known by God from the moment of its conception. David says in Psalm 139 verses 13-15 that God created that child within me, and all His works are wonderful. To consider my child as only a blob of cells whose loss doesn't matter, is denying the life-creating power of God. Besides I have thought of this 'blob of cells' as my baby for several weeks or months already, and it is impossible to think of it as anything less than a baby.

'God obviously never meant that child to be.'

This is the reaction I found hardest to deal with, and also one of the commonest I encountered. It resulted in many spiritual debates with God, and put Him in a negative light. If God never intended me to have this baby, why did He let me become pregnant in the first place? Did He miss the fact that I had become pregnant, and then think, 'Oh, dear! This baby isn't supposed to be born, we might as well get rid of it now!' I don't think so!

God originally intended a world where there was no sadness, where we could be fruitful and multiply, and where children would bring us joy. I don't believe God wants any baby to die. In the perfect world where God designed we should live, and in the heaven He is preparing for us now, God says He '"will wipe every tear from their eyes. There will be no more death or mourning or crying or pain,"' Revelation 21:4, NIV. In Isaiah 65:20, NIV, where there is another picture of heaven, God says, '"Never again will there be in it an infant that lives but a few days."'

I believe that God uses all the things that happen to us in this imperfect world 'for the good of those who love him,' Romans 8:28, NIV, but this may not be the most loving time to share such thoughts with a hurting mother. It is not really fair on God, or the parents of the baby, to make any comment implying that God could have caused the miscarriage, for whatever reason. The effects of sin in the world cause such tragedies. God cries with us when the sad things hurt. And He will eventually help us triumph over the most trying and painful circumstances.

'Just think, God has taken your baby to be one of His little cherubs in heaven!'

This is not a reaction that I heard, but a friend who did have this said to her was furious! She became angry with God for having taken her baby when He could so easily create any amount of cherubs He wanted, without having to 'steal' them from humans!

'Maybe there was something wrong with the baby, anyway?'

Yes, maybe there was. Miscarriage is nature's way of dealing with some of the occasional abnormalities. Often these are freak occurrences that will never happen again. In our case we did know that there was probably something wrong with the baby, as the doctor hadn't been able to detect a heartbeat. Even though these facts may be true, it's best to avoid giving this response. After a number of people had been saying this to us, I began to wonder; 'If there was something wrong with this baby, maybe there will be something wrong with another baby, too. Maybe we can't have normal children. If I do get pregnant again, then I'll be worried that there will be something seriously wrong with the baby.'

The fact is that women who miscarry are less likely to have a baby with an abnormality, because it seems that their bodies are more tuned to being selective at an early stage. But in the emotional aftermath of a miscarriage, this fact may not be much of a comfort either.

'Just think, now you'll be able to help all those other women who have miscarriages!'

Again, maybe true, but only if I can come to terms properly with my own experience of miscarriage. The problem with this approach was that I began to wonder what manner of other awful experiences I would have to encounter, just so I would be able to relate better to other suffering people! Visions of deformed children, widowhood and even cancer loomed large in my mind, and I wondered where it was all going to end!

'As a friend, what can I do to help someone who has had a miscarriage?'

As a friend, just be there. Try not to avoid the mother because you don't know what to say. She needs her friends. She needs to know that you love her, and that God loves her, and that you and God are both saddened by her loss.

You don't have to explain anything, or justify the loss, or make any of the comments outlined above. Just be there. Pray with her if you can. A simple prayer is enough: 'Dear Father, You know we are sad about the loss of Karen's baby, and You are sad too. Please touch us with your healing love. In Jesus' name, Amen.'

You may need to hug your friend and hold her a lot. This is very healing. If you have a baby of your own you may feel a bit uncomfortable, as if being there with your baby will cause her more pain. It will depend on your friend's own feelings, but one of the most healing moments I had a few weeks after the miscarriage was when a friend left a baby with me for a few minutes. I hugged the baby and rocked it, crying all the time, and it was as if I was hugging the baby I had lost, and showing my love for our baby in a tangible way, even though my own baby was gone. Yes, the presence of a baby may cause your friend to cry, but the chances are those tears will be very healing.

Don't be afraid of your friend's tears. She may cry. She may cry and cry. She may still be crying after several months or years. Always let her cry, hug her and love her, and accept her feelings.

Show you care, often, and in tangible ways. A well-chosen card, a small gift here and there, a phone call, or a shopping trip together. If she is collecting things for another future baby, find pretty little things for her to add to her collection.

Being with your friend in this way will often bind you together very closely, as there are few people who really know how to relate well to a woman who has miscarried. Other friends may withdraw, not knowing what to say; some friends may be saying things which are painful instead of healing; so you need to be there to show she still has friends she can trust.

Above all pray for your friend, and pray that God will show you how to be the best friend to her during this time. Each woman is different and will respond in a different way, and only God can help you know the best things to do.

CHAPTER NINE

Maintaining your marriage

BERNIE IS very different from me. He always seems so cool, calm and collected. I'm a crazy bundle of creative emotions. He takes it all just the way it comes, while I panic about possible dangers, pitfalls, problems and plagues. Every woman is different in the way she responds emotionally to a miscarriage. There may be some common experiences and feelings, but we are all unique. Your experience may be totally different from mine, and that's fine. Your experience may also be totally different from your partner's, and that's fine too.

Although we hadn't exactly anticipated having a pregnancy at that time in our lives, once we were aware of the possibility we were over the moon. Ever the romantic, I started a diary of my thoughts and emotions about the pregnancy and our baby. Bernie was busy studying and, as he wasn't actually pregnant, I don't think the full reality of a baby hit him with the wonderful force with which it hit me. We were both looking forward to parenthood, but to me the experience was more tangible.

Then all too sudden we were hurled into the horror of the miscarriage. I think if I had been able to go into hospital at an early stage, and been cared for there, Bernie would have been able to concentrate his attention on the emotional trauma of the situation. As it was, he had to cope with the practical side of the miscarriage and provide for my physical needs. In order to handle the situation from his perspective, he had to detach himself from the emotional implications of what was happening. Although he was always there for me, and was always comforting, he couldn't enter into the same emotions I was experiencing.

There were times when this was frustrating. Times when I would have liked us to cry together. I cried often at first, and one time it dawned on me that I was resenting the fact that Bernie couldn't cry about our loss in the same way I could. I think if he could, then it would have been a very healing experience for me. But Bernie is not like me. Although I know he is sad, he feels that deep inside, and doesn't express it openly in tears as I do. I realized that my resentment towards him could drive us apart, and cause me unnecessary anger. I had to learn to accept his way of expressing his feelings.

We came to a decision. It was easy for me to go into a corner and cry on my own, and feel isolated from Bernie, but we decided that this was an experience that could draw us even closer together, rather than force us apart. So, I would only cry when I could be with Bernie, and he could hold me tight, and I could talk about what was going through my mind. There were other times of tearfulness, when he couldn't be there, such as when I saw a baby in the street, or someone made a touching or thoughtless remark, and that couldn't be helped. But I would save the big sobs for Bernie. Slowly they subsided. We did come closer together, we prayed through the traumas and the resolution of our emotions, and slowly healing came again, to me and to us.

This is what Bernie has to say: 'My response to Karen's miscarriage was on a number of levels. Emotionally, I had not been very involved with the pregnancy. We had not planned to have a child at that time, and we had only known about the pregnancy for about nine weeks before the miscarriage. Besides, I am very much a take-it-or-leave-it personality, and it takes a while for the significance of an event (in this case the pregnancy) to sink in. As we were not planning on having a baby, having the miscarriage was, if anything, a relief from the responsibility of impending parenthood. Emotionally I could not grieve for a child that had not become a part of my dreams and reality.

'On the practical level, when Karen started threatening to miscarry I had to be the counsellor and first aider. Here was another person in crisis who needed support and practical help. I had spent some time as a hospital chaplain and have also done first aid, so I was able to cope quite well. However, it is more difficult when the person suffering is your own wife whom you love and don't wish to see suffer in any way.

'The major effect of the miscarriage on my life was trying to understand how seriously Karen was affected by the experience; and realizing that for her, twelve weeks of pregnancy had meant very concrete dreams. I also had to bring forward my ideal timing of our first child, because of Karen's great desire to have a child after the miscarriage. In summary, I suppose I was affected much more on a practical level, and less on an emotional level, and that reflects our separate approaches to life's events.'*

It is often hard for husbands to relate to the experience of a miscarriage. They may not have known about the pregnancy for as long as the mother has, and they do not have the physical union with the unborn child that a mother enjoys. For them the baby is some few months off into the future. The baby may seem quite intangible to the husband unless he has seen a scan, heard the heartbeat and felt a kicking foot, and often a miscarriage happens weeks before he can experience any of these wonderful things. In an attempt to respond and say something comforting, he may fall into the easy trap of making some of the comments discussed in chapter eight, and this can make the wife feel he doesn't understand her properly.

It is important for both the husband and the wife to be as honest as possible about their thoughts and feelings relating to the miscarriage. Without honesty all kinds of walls, hurts and misunderstandings can arise trying to push you both into a painful isolation from each other. Pray together and for each other. Spend time reading a book like this together, and discussing your responses. Make time for some special moments together; a meal out, a new outfit, a weekend away, an evening by the fireside.

Experiencing a miscarriage can cause both of you to question your own femininity or masculinity. It can make either parent feel somehow not quite complete as a person, and you each have to be sensitive to the other's most intimate needs. Take time to encourage each other, and to appreciate each other's uniqueness.

The husband may need to be extra patient for a few weeks until the doctor says it's all right to make love, and even then the wife may not feel like having full intercourse for a while. This is something for you to work out together, and the wife may need a lot of tenderness, treats and cuddles before she will feel confident enough to enjoy the experience of intimate love-making again.

One of the most dangerous things that can happen is when a husband or wife tries to blame the other for causing the miscarriage. It is often virtually impossible for the cause of a miscarriage to be identified, even by medical experts, so it is pointless for a couple to try and apportion blame in this way. It can start off so innocently: a casual remark, 'I wonder if you shouldn't have gone jogging that day before the miscarriage;' or 'I told you we shouldn't have made love that night, and you wouldn't listen to me.' Guilt and resentment can blow into astronomical heights and drive couples into divorces or emotional isolation. If the relationship does begin to suffer as a consequence of losing a baby, then try to find specialist help and counselling as soon as you can to mend the rift.

Things to keep in mind.
Each person responds to situations in very
    different ways.
Be loving, always.
Be tenderly honest with each other.
Share your feelings.
Do some special things together.
Appreciate each other.
Never apportion blame.

Understand that healing may take some time.

Avoid making thoughtless comments (see chapter eight).

Seek professional help if necessary.

------

*Bernie's reaction could also be an emotional defence mechanism by splitting off the facts and practicalities from the pain. Some women react like this too, and potentially this stores up trouble for later as the pain surfaces in another form — often unrecognized for what it is. Ed.

CHAPTER TEN

Coping with your family's reactions

WHEN ANNA found out that she was pregnant, she could hardly wait to call her parents and tell them the wonderful news! Their first grandchild! They were sure to be as over the moon as she and Robert were! On the surface they took the news well, though they were concerned about some of the practical issues, such as the fact that Robert and Anna still lived in rented accommodation, and Robert's job prospects were not secure. Robert's parents were delighted, but this would be their seventh grandchild, as Robert's three older sisters already had children.

Five weeks after Anna and Robert celebrated their good news, Anna began to spot. The bleeding became heavier, and she went into hospital. A scan showed that the foetus had already died, and a few hours later she had a full miscarriage.

Anna and Robert were devastated. It had never crossed their minds that such a thing could happen. They called their families again to tell them what had happened. Anna's parents were relieved. They were relatively young, still in their mid forties, and very active. The prospect of grandparenthood had shaken them profoundly, reminding them that their age was catching up with them. They had not fully adjusted to the idea by the time Anna lost her baby. It was hard for them to understand how she could be so sad about such a 'small' loss. Anna called, expecting a shoulder to cry on, and lots of sympathy, but she did not get it. Her father told her it wasn't a good time for her to have a baby anyway, and she should wait a few years till she and Robert could afford a home of their own.

Robert called his parents, also expecting sympathy. But there was no sympathy there either. What was wrong with Anna? Why couldn't she carry a baby to term? His mother had had four children, and none of his older sisters had ever miscarried. They even remarked that they had always thought Anna hadn't looked very strong, and this was proof. They would send her some special vitamins to take, to help build up her health.

Many parents respond very well when a tragedy such as a miscarriage hits their child's home. Both Anna's and Robert's parents had always been extremely supportive, and were still trying to be, in their own way. But grandparents can have their own mixed emotions about the loss of a foetal grandchild.

Some grandparents, like Anna's folks, may only feel relief at the news of the miscarriage, especially if they didn't know Anna and Robert were trying for a baby, or the pregnancy was unexpected, or even socially undesirable for them. Other grandparents may want to know what is wrong, and to have medical explanations for what has happened. Some fear the daughter-in-law may somehow be weakening the family genes. Others may be so devastated by the news themselves that they cannot offer the emotional support that the bereaved couple needs.

Even if one of the grandmothers has suffered a miscarriage in the past, her experience may not help her to respond to a grieving daughter, or daughter-in-law. In past generations, with unreliable birth control, a miscarriage may have been a welcome relief, not a tragic loss. And if the loss had been tragic, but the grandmother had not been able to work through her own emotions, then another miscarriage in the family could trigger the memories, and cause delayed grief. It is wonderful when a couple can find comfort in their own family circles, but this is not always the case. Sometimes the bereaved grandparents need to have information. They may need to read a book like this, or a medical leaflet given to you by the hospital, or a miscarriage support group.* They may need to hear exactly how the miscarriage has affected you personally, otherwise they cannot be expected to guess how you feel. You may like to invite them to a small memorial service for the baby, if you feel that is appropriate.

As Bernie and I were in America at the time of my miscarriage, we could not afford to have long conversations with our parents — in Britain — about what had happened. We told them briefly what had happened, and then wrote a letter explaining our experiences and emotions. Once they received our letter they could understand better what we had gone through, and were able to be very responsive.

Two of our siblings demonstrated their support and understanding for us in small, but very comforting ways. My brother Tim was in Australia when he found out I was going to have a baby. He was so delighted at the news that he went out into a park and yelled for joy! My mother wrote and told him that I had had a miscarriage, but he didn't know what that was. He wrote back, asking about it, and my mother explained that I had lost the baby. This time he was so devastated by the news that he had to take a day off work to recover! We only heard this second hand, but we felt encouraged by his spontaneous response to our tragedy. There was someone else out there who had also been deeply affected by the loss of our baby.

Bernie's sister was seven months pregnant when she heard of my miscarriage, and she wrote straight away, telling us how the news had affected her. Being pregnant, she could imagine how she would feel if she lost her own child, and her words were also a great comfort for us.

Relatives can easily fall into the trap of responding in some of the ways illustrated in chapter eight. If they do, then you may need to explain, gently, the potential effect of what they are saying. Or you may choose to accept their remarks as their own way of showing concern. This will depend on how you feel, who the relative is, and on the closeness of your relationship with them. Your bachelor great-uncle Sidney may not really want to know all the medical and emotional details, and other relatives from older generations were brought up not to discuss such intimate matters. So you may need to use your discretion about whom you will tell what!

If you already have other children, they deserve a reasonable and appropriate explanation of what has happened. Even very young children are sensitive to their parents' emotions, and can pick up that something has been happening, especially if mummy went to the hospital, and is now very sad. You may need to explain that mummy had a tiny baby growing inside of her that has now died, and gone away, and so you are sad. Your child may need reassuring that she cannot die that way, or 'go away' as this baby did. You can say that the baby probably had something very wrong with it, so it could not grow like a normal baby, or explain simply whatever the reason may have been for the miscarriage. Be wary of saying that the baby 'went to sleep' and didn't wake up, or the child may become afraid of going to sleep, too. Telling them that God has taken the baby to be an angel in heaven can also be dangerous, as the child may build up resentment towards God for taking their baby away.

Children can have strong beliefs that their wishes will come true, if they wish them strongly enough, and if they ever 'wished the baby away', or had feelings of resentment towards your pregnancy, a miscarriage can make them feel they have destroyed the baby, and lead to intense feelings of guilt. They may not have expressed their true feelings about your pregnancy, so reassure them that nothing they did caused the miscarriage. They may also need reassurance of this if they were ever told, 'be careful of mummy's tummy', as they could think they squashed the baby, or hurt it by hugging mummy.

We experienced two miscarriages before we had our first baby. After that, we always explained to the other children that sometimes things go wrong and babies can die before they are born, but we hope and pray that the new baby will be all right. Maybe we are too cautious, but it helps ease the way if ever there is a problem during the pregnancy. Our eldest child preceded all remarks and questions about the unborn baby with: 'Mummy, if the baby doesn't die, . . . ' much to the shocked amazement of any unsuspecting eavesdroppers!

Answer any questions the child may have as fully, as honestly and as simply as you can. Plan to do some special things with your children, remembering that they need to have fun even if you may not feel too wonderful, but don't take on anything too strenuous for a few weeks after the miscarriage. Check that you are not becoming so self-absorbed in your grief that you are neglecting to respond adequately to the children you already have.

FINDING A MISCARRIAGE SUPPORT GROUP

Usually a miscarriage support group has a local phone number, and you can call anytime, and someone will be there to talk to, to listen, and offer support, understanding and information. You will almost always be talking to another woman who has also experienced a miscarriage, and has been trained to help you. Often there are a number of women who run the phone-line, and they may meet on a regular basis. They usually have contact with various professionals who can offer help and advice if necessary.

Immediately after a miscarriage is often a time when you could benefit from finding a support group, or talking to a helpline. The sooner you find people to share your emotions with, and who will be able to answer your questions and help you understand what has happened, the better. If you do feel isolated and lonely and need to talk to someone who you feel will really understand, then try to seek out a miscarriage support group.

Start enquiries at your local hospital, where ante- and post-natal care takes place. Local groups often leave their information leaflets with nursing staff, and chaplains, so ask them first. If they don't know of any groups then try the phone book, library, community information services, etc. There may be national organizations in your country that provide information and support after a miscarriage, and they may know of local people whom you can contact.

If there are no support groups or helplines in your area maybe you could think about starting one, but wait until you have come to terms with your own miscarriage first. You can place an advertisement in a local paper for women who have had miscarriages, and wish to be involved in supporting others. Meet together as a group to decide what you can do. Find some supportive nursing and medical staff to be part of your group, and see if a national miscarriage organization can provide useful training and materials. This will take a lot of energy and time, so be sure you are aware of what you are taking on before you venture into a potentially major commitment. It may also cost money to set up the helpline, though check your local phone company, as they may be able to offer special help to charities. Many women need to talk to others who have been through the same experiences of miscarriage, and don't know where to turn. You could help to provide them with the support and a listening ear that they so badly need.

In Britain, The Miscarriage Association has information about local helpline numbers and groups, provides information sheets, and a quarterly newsletter, and has speakers available. (See Appendix.)

CHAPTER ELEVEN

Beginning again

EVEN WHILE I was still going through the stages of grief, I was beginning to pick up the pieces and make a new start. I think I would have liked to have become pregnant straight away, but after our doctor had advised us to wait for a few months I was too afraid of another miscarriage to disobey his advice. So we knew we had to live through a frustrating few months before we could even try for another baby. I realized the waiting time was going to be difficult, and was wondering how best to cope with it. Suddenly, one day, it came to me! 'Bernie,' I announced, 'I've got something to tell you! I'm pre-pregnant!'

'Pre-pregnant?' Bernie sounded understandably perplexed. Now what was happening to his crazy wife?

'Well, rather than just wait around doing nothing, I can be pre-pregnant and take the time to prepare really well for another baby. It's a way to try and cope with this nothingness-time, and turn it into something positive.'

After a miscarriage, waiting to be pregnant again can be a very challenging time, filled with self-doubt, impatience, fear and frustration, none of which are particularly healthy, although they may all be quite natural responses. The concept of pre-pregnancy can help to focus your thoughts and attention towards more positive things, which will also help you to be more healthy the next time around. Once you start to think of creative ways to handle this special time, you will probably come up with quite a few things you can do. Here are just a few that we tried.

Healthy life-style

Studies are beginning to show how important it is for both parents to be healthy for several months before conceiving a child. So this is a good time to start making any changes that are necessary. Definitely avoid smoking and alcohol and discuss any drugs your doctor may want to prescribe for either of you very carefully with him first, explaining your situation. Make sure you clear up any infections, and be sure that you have immunity against rubella (German measles), as contact with this disease during the first few months of pregnancy can have catastrophic consequences. Avoid coffee and tea, too, where possible, as these contain caffeine which can have a powerful effect on the nervous system of an unborn child.

Eat plenty of fresh fruit and vegetables, and cut down on excess fats. Doctors are continually preparing new lists of foods which pregnant women should avoid, so check up on the latest information and get started now. If you feel you need to, you may like to start taking vitamins especially designed for pregnant women. Why not begin your antenatal exercise routines now? Then they'll be easier to manage in pregnancy too. Also get plenty of rest and sleep, fresh air and sunshine. Enjoy the feeling of well-being, you never know how sick you may feel once you actually become pregnant, so make the most of feeling good now! 'Foresight' is a British charity which can offer plenty of advice on preparing for a pregnancy. (See Appendix.)

Gather things for a new baby

Not everyone feels able to collect little items for an unborn, or even unconceived, child. There is a sort of old wives' taboo that if you do, things are bound to go wrong. Personally I found it wonderful to go into shops and buy little things for a future baby. It gave me a lot of happiness at a time when everything else seemed a little gloomy. There was hope in the tiny dresses and underwear that one day I would have a baby who would wear such lovely things. But I also told myself that, even if I never had a baby, there would be a child somewhere who would love to have such things. I also secretly wished other people might give me some little things for a baby 'hope chest', but no one did. I understood why not, but I still wished. I think I needed to feel that other people had the same hopes as me, that I would have a baby one day, but maybe they thought such a gift would offend or hurt me in some way. Not until I was going through a rough pregnancy with our daughter did someone buy me a baby gift. It was so precious to me, and gave me hope again when doubts and fears could easily have crept back.

Do things together as a couple

Plan some special times together as a couple. Once you have a new baby it will be harder to take time just for each other, so go for walks together, eat out, have a weekend away. Spend time talking and sharing, so that this time will bring you even closer together. Be honest and open about your feelings towards the miscarriage, and the thought of another pregnancy. Encourage and build each other up. Show your love in tangible ways. Your shared experience of the loss of your baby can bring you closer together, rather than push you apart, but the key is open communication, otherwise one of you may withdraw into an atmosphere of hurt and isolation which is potentially destructive.

If you already have children, take time to do some special things with them, too. Take trips out, go on picnics, have a party, plan fun evenings at home together.

Minimize the stress in your lives

Are there things in your life-style that are causing you stress, irritating you, using up energy you feel you can't afford to lose? Sit down and make a list of them, and then see how many you can minimize or eliminate. Have you been taking on too many responsibilities and activities at work, church, or in your social lives? Are there projects you would like to see completed before you think about trying for a baby again? Do you need to move house, or do major redecorating in your present home? Would you like to do some adventurous travelling together before finally settling down to family life? All these are things which you have time to do something about before getting pregnant again.

If you have never had a baby before, it is easy for you both to underestimate the amount of time and energy that a tiny baby can consume. It's easy to think that the baby will sleep a lot and you'll have plenty of time to completely refurbish your crumbling Victorian terrace, write a book, study for your degree or whatever. Getting major tasks out of the way before you are pregnant again will be well worth the effort in the long run. I had thought I would have plenty of time to stitch a patchwork quilt for our first baby, once I was pregnant. I was so sick that I finished it only days before delivering her. A friend of ours decided to get pregnant during her Masters degree, so she could settle down to motherhood afterwards. She was so ill she could barely study, and nearly jeopardized her chances of completing her course successfully.

Prepare yourselves for parenthood

Now is an excellent time to do all that reading on aspects of parenthood! Search your library and Christian book shop for good books by leading Christian authors on parenting. Dr. James Dobson is a good place to start. Subscribe to Christian marriage and family magazines. Watch videos on family life. Go on parenting seminars (if you can find any!). Borrow a baby for a day! One mother once told me to read all I could before having a baby, 'Once you have a baby, you'll have no time—and if you do find time to read the books, they'll only make you feel guilty!' So read them now before you have any parenting experiences you might regret!

Prepare yourself emotionally

After a miscarriage you can experience a plethora

of emotions. You will probably be affected by these for many years, maybe a whole lifetime, but it is good if you have come through the stages of grief outlined in some of the previous chapters before embarking on another pregnancy. It is important to remember that a new baby will not replace the one that was lost. Each child is individual and unique, and needs to be accepted as such. It is healing to go through a pregnancy and produce a healthy baby and feel you are 'normal', but it is vital that you have worked through your reactions to your grief, and strengthened your relationships with those around you. If you find that healing is taking longer than you would like, don't hesitate to seek counselling from your doctor, pastor, professional counsellor, or specialist midwife. They can help you structure your recovery, facilitate healing, and clarify your responses.

Prepare yourself spiritually

The chances are that your spiritual life may have taken a nosedive as you have ridden an emotional roller-coaster, and encountered feelings of anger, grief, loneliness, confusion and helplessness. You have probably yelled, 'Why?' at God. Your faith may have crumbled. You may have felt God had let you down. The responses of those in your church may have disappointed you. As a parent you are going to need God more than you've ever needed Him before! You may need to take time to ask for forgiveness. You may need to spend time growing spiritually, and rebuilding your relationship with Him. Psalm 103 portrays a beautiful picture of God. Read it over and over. List all the things it tells you about God's relationship with you. Share your spiritual growth with your husband, so that you can grow together. He may have had a lot of questions about God because he has watched you suffer.

Begin praying now about your future. Ask God's guidance about future plans for a family. Pray for your potential children. Think about what you want for your children. Pray for your home. And, hardest of all maybe, pray for contentment and happiness, no matter what the future holds.

CHAPTER TWELVE

Where do I go from here?

I DON'T KNOW when the really intense feelings of loss and grief began to subside. It was a slow process of ups and downs. Some days I would have a strong sense of loneliness, because, in a strange sort of way, the baby had kept me company. Just knowing there was a secret life within me had given me many moments of quiet, glowing happiness and gentle thrills, and now there was only emptiness and sadness. The tiniest, unseen bundle of life can bring with its awareness so many hopes and dreams to a mother, and I had to grieve for their loss too.

There would be days when I would seem to cope perfectly well, managing a demanding job, a houseful of guests, and packing for a move. Other days some small thing: the cry of a baby; a toy shop window; finding my maternity clothes; or just nothing at all, would send me into a downward spiral of thoughts and indescribable emotions. Indescribable because they were so complex, such a mixture of tears, loneliness, broken dreams, fears for future pregnancies, frustrations . . . a cocktail of powerful sensations.

The ups and downs diluted themselves in a trans-Atlantic move, giving up a job with incredible potential, and re-establishing ourselves back in England. The downs increased again as we tried for another baby, with predictable monthly slumps each time our failure became apparent. As soon as we had registered with a doctor I went along to see him. 'A few months ago I had a miscarriage, and I was wondering what I should do to prepare for another pregnancy. Have you got any advice for me about diet, or anything else I should do to be as healthy as possible, please?'

'Well, if you're not pregnant within the next year, come back and I'll refer you to an infertility support group.' I was shocked by his insensitive response. It was hard enough coping with the miscarriage, waiting for three long months to try again, and even just a few repeated failures had left me emotionally struggling. The daunting prospect of complete infertility rose again before me. I decided that if ever I should get pregnant, I didn't want to be faced with him as a doctor. I went home and transferred to another practice with a Christian lady doctor.

About this time our church had a Mothers' Day service. I hadn't known it was going to take place, because someone else had been arranging it. For me it was the worst Mother's Day ever. I know no one had meant me to be hurt at all, and if they had known how I was responding emotionally, I know they would have made provision for me. . . . Anyway, two children came into the congregation bearing baskets of posies for every mother. Every woman in that small church received some flowers, except me. I thought of our tiny child. I *was* a mother! Just because no one knew of our loss, it didn't make me any less of a mother. I was furious and at the same time distraught. I went to the ladies' room and sobbed and sobbed, and only Bernie knew.

Now as we pastor other churches, if ever there is a special service honouring mothers, we make sure *every* woman is included, and talk about the ways in which *all* women can 'mother' and bring comfort and care to others in a variety of ways, whether they are married or single, young or old, and whether or not they have children. Our experience taught us that what is meant to be a simple, happy occasion, full of beauty and flowers and love, can be a nightmare. Especially for someone who is struggling with childlessness, or the loss of a child, or for someone who has had an abortion or miscarriage.

Then I found another job, not one I really wanted, but it would have to do. A few days before I started work, I realized I was pregnant again.

I went to work the first day and felt really strange. I thought it was just the strain of adjusting to a new environment, and trying to take in the masses of information being thrust at me. At lunchtime I discovered I was losing again. This was when I had my second miscarriage (see chapter six).

A month or so later we finally managed to conceive again. As soon as our doctor knew I was pregnant, she made an appointment for me with a specialist. First, I had an ultra-sound scan at about seven weeks to check that I was carrying a viable foetus, and then he prescribed weekly hormone injections that would help to boost my own hormones. He said that at the moment no one could be sure that such injections really helped, but that they would not do any harm, and it was worth a try. I also left with strict instructions about not working until I was four months pregnant, not lifting heavy things, not even cleaning the bath and doing the vacuuming! I was so sick I could barely think. I couldn't even read for the first three months: there was certainly no danger of me 'doing too much'! The slightest exertion or whiff of food was enough to trigger a bout of vomiting! So much for all those romantic notions of pregnancy! My 'morning sickness' lasted all day, every day, for nine months!

That sickness was so intense and horrible that I could almost have prayed for a miscarriage to bring me some relief! The only thought that held me back was that I'd only have to go through all the sickness again, anyway, if I ever wanted to have a baby.

Finally, on my due date, baby Bethany arrived weighing in at just over 4kg (9lbs 4oz). Two-and-a-half years later baby Nathan arrived after an even more nauseous pregnancy! Another three years and Joel was born after the worst pregnancy of all! So we finally had our babies. But even now, on occasion, my mind replays all the events of that lonely September night. Sometimes I still cry for the babies I never cuddled and never saw. And sometimes I still pray that one day we will see our lost children and let them know just how much they were loved and wanted.

During each of my pregnancies the miscarriage experience has come back to haunt me. I find myself putting off going to the toilet, afraid of what I may find, and I always carry something with me in case I start to bleed. When I begin to feel the baby move, I relax, but if I notice a few hours without a kick, I wonder if anything has gone wrong.

For years I asked God 'Why?'. 'Why couldn't I see

the tiny baby? Why was its little body flushed away even though we had tried so hard to save it?' Those questions haunted me for about four years. As I kept on asking, I began to feel a stronger sense of God saying, 'Because I love you, because you'd gone through enough already.' Then I came to the realization that if we had found that there was something horribly wrong with the baby, such as a major deformity, or that it lacked a brain, I would have lived with a greater fear of having another baby with similar problems. I don't know all the details, but I have come to the place where I know, without a doubt, God was acting in my best interests.

A friend was telling me about her experiences in starting a telephone helpline for mothers who had experienced a miscarriage. One 80-year-old lady called and said that she had had a miscarriage when she was 20. At the time everyone said the usual things to her: 'Pull yourself together, and get on with life, dear'; 'Oh, you'll soon have another one'; and so on. So she never spoke about her experiences to anyone for sixty years, 'But,' she told my friend, 'in sixty years I have never forgotten, for all this time I have been crying inside, and sometimes outside too, when no one was around. Now you have let me talk about it, and listened, and understood. Now I'm beginning to feel some healing inside. I wish you'd been here sixty years ago.'

Sometimes, when talking to other women, I feel impressed to mention the fact that I have experienced miscarriage. Time and again someone has then felt free to share their own secret sadness. I am constantly amazed at how many women have had a miscarriage, and yet so few feel able to talk about their emotions, until they find someone else who they know will understand. And then all the feelings flow out, bottled up for months or years, and the healing can begin. But that doesn't mean they will ever forget. I don't think you ever can forget. The experience of giving birth at nine months, or nine weeks, is always a very intense experience in a woman's life. Intense experiences like that become somehow engraved on your heart and mind, recorded in such a way that they can never be erased, using a four-dimensional technique, where the fourth dimension is emotion. But time can help put those experiences and emotions into different perspectives, and into a framework where healing can occur. And, eventually, you can remember, and talk about your miscarriage without the intense pain and emotion that there was initially.

In the meantime, as a mother watching Bethany, Nathan and Joel grow, I know that my greatest desire for all of us, as a family, is to live a life that will prepare us, and hopefully others too, for a life in heaven, together for eternity, where there won't be any heartbreaks, any lonely sadnesses, any lost babies. Where all our tears will be wiped away by a loving God, who never intended that we should be anything other than happy, loving and loved.

Appendix

A list of organizations who may be able to help you. Please send a large stamped, self-addressed envelope with any enquiry you may make to the following organizations. Include stamps to cover the current cost of posting 100g. The charities will appreciate your thoughtfulness. Thank you.

GREAT BRITAIN
Miscarriage Association
c/o Clayton Hospital, Northgate, Wakefield, West Yorks, WF1 3JS. Tel. (0924) 200799.

Information and support for women who have experienced a miscarriage, or who threaten to. Also information for, and education of, professionals and lay people about the implications of a miscarriage. The Association can provide information sheets on a range of topics, and a quarterly newsletter. They can also put you in touch with local groups and contacts, and provide speakers. Please enclose an SAE with all enquiries.

SANDS – Stillbirth and Neonatal Death Society
28 Portland Place, London, W1N 4DE. Helpline tel. (071) 436 5881.

Support through self-help groups, and befriending bereaved parents who have experienced a pregnancy loss, stillbirth, or neonatal death. Aims to make the public and professionals more aware of the emotional needs of the parents. Provides information booklets, and will tell you of local groups. Good source of information if you wish to have a burial or funeral.

Well-Being
27 Sussex Place, Regents Park, London, NW1 4SP. Tel. (071) 262 5337.

Funds medical research into better health for mothers and babies, and has information about the latest research into miscarriage, and help available to women who miscarry repeatedly.

British Pregnancy Advisory Service
7 Belgrave Road, London, SW1. Tel. (071) 222 0985.

Secular organization with branches throughout Britain (see your local phone book). Can provide counselling through difficult pregnancies, and information.

Issue – National Fertility Association
509 Aldridge Road, Great Barr, Birmingham, B44 8NA. Tel. (021) 344 4414.

Self-help group for people with impaired fertility, and difficulties starting a family. Provides contacts, counselling, leaflets and information on infertility.

Foresight — Association for the Promotion of Preconceptual Care
28 The Paddock, Godalming, Surrey, GU7 1XD. Tel. (0483) 427839.

Help for couples preparing for pregnancy, testing for nutritional deficiencies, and other factors which could harm the unborn child. Counselling on diet, life-style and health.

UNITED STATES OF AMERICA

As organizations vary from state to state, and city to city, it is best to check with your local hospital about local chapters and support groups.